Lighthouses of England and Wales

BISHOP ROCK

by

Martin Boyle

B & T Publicati

D0259850

1

PUBLISHED BY B & T PUBLICATIONS,
10 Orchard Way, Highfield, Southampton.
Hampshire SO17 1RD

International Standard Book Number

ISBN 1-901043-05-3

International Standard Serial Number

ISSN 1363 8009

Printed by Bishop's Printers (01705) 825883
Typesetting by Micrographics (01983) 853658

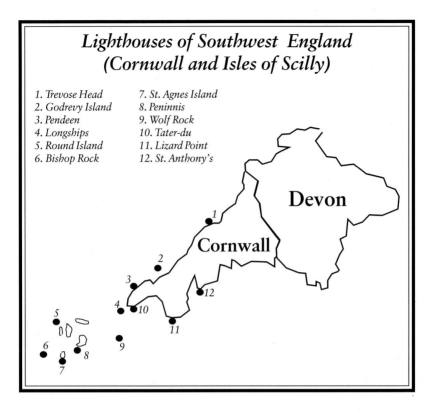

Lighthouses of Southwest England
(Cornwall and Isles of Scilly)

1. Trevose Head
2. Godrevy Island
3. Pendeen
4. Longships
5. Round Island
6. Bishop Rock

7. St. Agnes Island
8. Peninnis
9. Wolf Rock
10. Tater-du
11. Lizard Point
12. St. Anthony's

Devon

Cornwall

SPECIAL ACKNOWLEDGEMENT

The author gratefully acknowledges the invaluable help of the Corporation of Trinity House, its Publication Officer and Media Director, its Director of Engineering and his exceptional Staff, with the full co-operation of the Master and Elder Brethren

3

Contents   Page No

BISHOP ROCK

POSITION: 49° 52' 05" N - 06° 26' 06" W
LOCATION: Extreme westerly rock - Isles of Scilly
NO. ON ADMIRALTY LIST OF LIGHTS: 0002
PRESENT TOWER BUILT: 1887
TOWER STRUCTURE: Granite
DESIGNER: Sir James Nicholas Douglass
FOCAL HEIGHT OF LIGHT: 144ft. 3ins. (44m) A.H.W.S.T.
FIRST LIT: 25th October 1887
AUTOMATION DATE: 12th December 1992
MONARCH AT TIME OF CONSTRUCTION: Queen Victoria (1837 - 1901)

BISHOP ROCK

Who Named It?

Bishop Rock is believed to have been officially named during the 15th to 16th century, because of its distinctive shape of a *'Bishop's Mitre'*. Its dark pink colour also adds to the final touch of credibility. Some references actually imply that the Rock was named as part of the *'Bishop's and Clerks'* reef. In fact this area is near the South Bishop lighthouse off the Pembrokeshire coast in Wales.

There has even been an element of folklore which seems to have derived from the medieval times. Apparently; as the story goes, the head of the religious order on the Isles of Scilly during the 12th and 13th century, also doubled as the Bishop and local law enforcement officer. This notable person is said to have sent out felons who only had a *'pitcher of ale and black bread'* to stay overnight on the Rock as a punishment. If on the following morning the offender was still on the Rock, it was classified as *'God's judgement'* that he was forgiven. When considering the dangerous seas around this area it seems impossible that anyone would have survived. Also it seems this is purely a *'made-up story'*, because it is most certainly not creditable that anyone would even attempt to go through these treacherous waters and hidden obstacles to put a man on the Bishop Rock in the first place.

Trinity House chose the Bishop Rock for the site of a much needed maritime light, because it is the extreme westerly outcrop of the Isles of Scilly. This Rock is also the most prominent outcrop on the Western Reef, which covers an area of nearly ten square miles.

The Wrecking of the ROYAL OAK

Among the numerous ships which have been wrecked around the Isles of Scilly, the first recorded incident that referred to the Bishop Rock was the ROYAL OAK on the 18th January 1666. A report following this disaster was sent by one of her junior officers, Mr. Daniels, to the shipowners. In it he stated that there was no cause for the tragedy. Captain Robb Locke, the ROYAL OAK'S Master, ordered some of his men to go topside, to see if there was a clear passage through the reef. With darkness surrounding the vessel, it was impossible to fix a safe course, so Captain Locke ordered the main front anchor to be dropped. But as soon as the anchor took hold, a huge wave spun the ROYAL OAK and smashed her against the rocks. In order to reduce the top weight of his stricken ship, Captain Locke ordered his crew to chop down the masts. But this action was too late. A further onslaught of waves pounded the helpless vessel onto the rocks.

Within a few minutes the ROYAL OAK was a total wreck. From a complement of 32 crew, only 8 survived. Mr. Daniels was one of these men, who along with the other survivors, scrambled to the nearest low rock for safety. But within minutes the relentless waves had washed them back into the sea. Frantically they swam towards sections of wreckage, which miraculously carried them to the relative safety of the Bishop Rock. Most of these men were badly injured or bleeding and for comfort they huddled together on the slippery Rock.

From the night of the 18th January until the early morning of the 20th, the survivors of the ROYAL OAK clung to the Bishop Rock. When barrels of pepper and pieces of wreckage were washed ashore at St. Mary's Island, the Mayor, Edward Roscaricke, ordered rescue boats to go out and search for survivors. By midday Mr. Daniels and the remaining crewmen were saved. After spending nearly 52 hours on the Bishop Rock, most of these men were suffering from exposure, with their arms and legs swollen up from the cold or their injuries. [8]

St. Agnes Lighthouse

Prior to the building of the 74ft (22.6m) high St. Agnes lighthouse in 1680, there were no beacons or navigational lights around the Isles of Scilly. Sir John Clayton petitioned the Privy Council of Charles II, for the right to erect the St. Agnes lighthouse and the authority to levy shipping by compulsory means for its upkeep. However, Trinity House were strongly opposed to any privately owned lights, especially those proposed by Sir John Clayton. In response to this petition, the Corporation offered to provide

The lighthouse on St. Agnes Island.
Note the Bishop Rock lighthouse in the right background
Photograph by Andrew Gibson and reproduced by kind permission of F.E. Gibson

a lighthouse on St. Agnes without any profits. Because of this, Sir John Clayton's petition was refused.

Two elder Brethren of Trinity House built the St. Agnes lighthouse, which was officially lit on the 30th October 1680. These two men, Captain Bayley and Captain Tiel, constructed the lighthouse with its light set at 138ft (42m) AHWST. However its light was still obscured by the islands, which made it virtually useless for shipping near the Western Rocks. [10]

H.M.S. ROMNEY - 400 Dead

Even the English Navy saw the tragic loss of a ship and nearly 400 men, on the 22nd October 1707. This disaster was part of a larger tragedy, which involved a fleet of warships under the Command of Admiral Sir Cloudisley Shovell. Close to the Bishop Rock lies one of these fated ships, H.M.S. ROMNEY. [8]

H.M.S. ROMNEY was a 50 gun frigate, which was part of a fleet of warships returning from Toulon. On the 21st October 1707, this fleet was blown off course during a storm. Admiral Shovell, sent word to the Commanders of the other ships, ordering them to come onboard his flagship ASSOCIATION, to fix their present position. During the briefing the majority vote was in favour of a position near to the coast of France. The Master of the LENNOX, Captain Sir William Tumper, disagreed with the decision and for the record he strongly believed they were close to the Isles of Scilly.

Admiral Shovell ordered part of his fleet, led by the LENNOX, to proceed ahead on a north-easterly course, which was assumed would take them to Falmouth. A few hours later the ROMNEY followed the ASSOCIATION; along with the remainder of the fleet, on a similar course as the LENNOX. At 22:00 on the 22nd October 1707, the ROMNEY hit the Western Rocks at full sail, about half a mile (805m) from the Bishop Rock. From a complement of nearly 400 men, only the quartermaster survived.

Bearing in mind the magnitude of the larger disaster involving Admiral Shovell's fleet, which saw the death of nearly 2000 men, it seems strange that some means of lighting the Western Rocks was not implemented for about 140 years. During this time numerous vessels and countless lives were lost on this treacherous reef. In many cases there were no records of these vessels, with the only indication of their loss near the Isles of Scilly being shown by the wreckage washed up along the shorelines. [8]

THEODORICK - WILLIAM PRESTON - NIEKERIE and DURORO

On the 4th September 1839, the THEODORICK became the first reported vessel to actually hit the Bishop Rock. The weather conditions were severe, with a heavy mist. This merchant ship's cargo was classified as 'General'.

Within minutes of hitting the Bishop Rock, she sank with the loss of everyone aboard. Close to this wreck lies another vessel, the WILLIAM PRESTON, which sank on its maiden voyage from Odessa, after hitting the Bishop Rock in February 1842. Once more the deadly sea claimed the lives of everyone on board. Less than twelve months later, the 600 ton paddle steamer BRIGAND, left Liverpool for St. Petersburgh, on the evening tide of the 10th October. By 05:00 on the 12th, her lookout spotted the St. Agnes light. As the BRIGAND continued her voyage, she suddenly hit the Bishop Rock at full speed. On impact, one of her paddle wheels was smashed into the engine room. Although a fire broke out it was quickly extinguished by the sudden rush of water that entered the gaping hole in her side. [8]

Luckily the BRIGAND had four watertight compartments, of which two were undamaged. As a result she remained afloat for a further two hours. This allowed the strickened steamer to drift closer to a landfall, before sinking in 45 fathoms of water. During this period, her Master Captain Hunt and his crew of 27, managed to crowd into the two remaining lifeboats and reach the safety of St. Mary's Island.

Although slavery was officially made illegal in Britain in 1807, one particular ship was wrecked near the Bishop Rock almost 36 years later, which proved that this cruel activity was still in operation.

On the 27th January 1843, the Liverpool built 400 ton barque, DURORO was returning from America when she hit the Crebawethen Rock at full sail. Wreckage was washed ashore at St. Mary's Island, but none of her crew of 15 men were ever found.

It was known that the DURORO had a cargo on board, which was classed as *'bailed goods, armoury and brass stops.'* However between 1841 and 1842 various Coastguard and Liverpool Customs officers had searched the barque in her home port, following several reports that her Captain was actively engaged in the illegal transportation of immigrants and smuggling. Yet on each occasion when the vessel was thoroughly searched, nothing was found.

In 1973 a diving team from Weymouth in Dorset, accidentally found the DURORO about a mile from the Bishop Rock. Amongst the wreckage was found several casks which contained manillas. These high quality copper bands or rings were originally worn to signify positions of status by the west coast Africans. They were also used by the natives as a means of currency. It is also known that only those people who were actively involved with the capture of slaves, would have the manillas in their possession. These copper bands were then used by the *'slavers'* to pay the local African natives who assisted in the capture and enslavement work.

The desperate need for a light to cover the Western Rocks, was finally demonstrated by the sinking of the NIEKERIE, on the 21st February 1844. This Rotterdam barque was en route from Batavia, bound for her home

James Walker's iron pile tower of 1850
Reproduced with kind permission of Trinity House

port. She hit the Western Rocks, just a short distance from the Bishop Rock, carrying a cargo of coffee and sugar. Of her Master, Captain Haweg and his crew of 19, only the sailmaker Simon Greve and seaman Christian Soupe survived. They were picked up by a passing Cornish fishing boat 12 hours later, after being found clinging to part of the wreckage. [8]

James Walker's Fated Tower

With deadly regularity, by the middle of the 19th century the number of ships being wrecked around the Western Rocks had reached epidemic proportions. Shipowners and merchants of many nations demanded that the Corporation of Trinity House should provide a suitable navigational light. In theory this idea seemed simple, but in practise it was one of the most treacherous projects to be undertaken.

Trinity House instructed its consultant engineer, James Walker FRS, to prepare the designs, plans and estimates for erecting a lighthouse on the Bishop Rock. On the 15th April 1847, James Walker and his partner John Burges, went to the proposed site to carry out a full survey. After considering many options they decided to adopt the principal of a pile lighthouse, similar in design as those devised by Alexander Mitchell. James Walker believed that if a lighthouse could withstand the forces of the sea when built on piles on a sandy sea-bed, then his adaption would be infinitely stronger if erected on a rock foundation. [1]

Full approval was given by the Lords of the Privy Council of Trade and the Corporation of Trinity House, for the Bishop Rock project to begin. Nicholas Douglass was appointed as the Superintendent Engineer, with his eldest son James designated as the Assistant Engineer for the contract. The Douglass workforce began the project during the summer of 1848, with the arduous task of drilling large holes into the surface of the Bishop Rock. A central stanchion, 3ft 6ins (1.06m) in diameter, was to be surrounded by an octagonal formation of iron legs. Access to the lighthouse cabin would be through a cast iron doorway set at the base of the hollow stanchion and up a steel ladder fixed inside. The lighthouse cabin would consist of cast iron plates riveted together, with a coal burning brazier set on top of the cabin's cast steel roof.

The perilous work continued during the summer seasons for nearly three years, until the lighthouse was completed apart from the positioning of its lantern. On the night of the 5th February 1850 a ferocious storm ravaged the Isles of Scilly, felling trees and demolishing houses. By the following morning the partly completed lighthouse had been washed away. Nicholas Douglass and his disheartened workforce had to wait nearly ten days because of the weather, before they could return to the Bishop Rock. All that remained of three years of backbreaking work, were the snapped-off stumps of the stanchion and its iron legs. [1]

PLAN
FOR PROPOSED LIGHTHOUSE FOR THE
BISHOP ROCK

SECTION

Plan of the proposed cast-iron lighthouse for the Bishop Rock.
Reproduced with kind permission of Trinity House

A New Granite Tower

James Walker wrote to the Elder Brethren of Trinity House on the 9th February 1850, in which he reported the failure of his tower. He stated that the situation might have been worse, if the keepers had been in residence at the time. Following this disastrous setback, it would seem that confidence in James Walker's design capabilities might be in question. But this was not the case. The Elder Brethren accepted the regrettable incident and commissioned him to design and construct another lighthouse, this time out of Cornish granite. Nicholas Douglass; now 50 years old, was again appointed Superintendent Engineer, but with John McConnochie given the position of Resident Engineer. His son, James Douglass was appointed the assistant engineer for the contract. John McConnochie was chosen because of his extensive knowledge of working with granite. [1]

Nicholas Douglass - James Douglass - John McConnochie

In May 1850, Nicholas Douglass obtained permission to build a number of houses on the uninhabited island of Rosevear. This island had already been used during the previous Bishop Rock contract, but these new stone dwellings would replace the temporary timber sheds which had been erected at that time. Work commenced on the Bishop Rock at the beginning of July, with the difficult task of preparing the dovetailed indentations to the surface of the Rock. While this part of the project progressed, James Douglass was given the job of organising the granite for the tower. All of this stone was supplied by the Carnsew and Lamorna quarries in Cornwall. In its rough-cut state, the granite was shipped to St. Mary's where it was dressed according to templates, before shipment to Rosevear Island. [1]

However, in his book 'Sixty Years of the Scilly Isles', Robert Maybee stated that the granite was actually dressed on Rat Island, which conflicts with the details specified in the 'Minutes of the Institution of Civil Engineers'. During the first year of the Bishop Rock contract the prepared granite was shipped to Resevear Island on board the BILLOW, but from the second year this work was carried out by the tug BISHOP, which towed the dressed stone in barges.

Back Breaking Work & The Survivors of the BELINDA

In appalling conditions the John McConnochie and James Douglass workforce continued with the back breaking work, until the solid base of the Bishop Rock tower was 46ft (14m) AHWST. On numerous occasions the men were washed off the Rock by the sea. For the conditions in which they were employed, it seems strange the only a few of the workforce were able to swim. It was noted by one of the masons, that James Douglass was always one of the first people to dive into the sea and assist with any rescue. [3]

By November 1852, a total of 44 granite blocks had been positioned on the Bishop Rock, each weighing between 2 or 3 tons. At this stage of the contract James Douglass was appointed Resident Engineer for another project, with his position taken over by his brother William. On completion of his two year appointment in June 1854 James Douglass returned to the Bishop Rock, following John McConnochie being posted to another Walker and Burges contract. From this time James Douglass became the Resident Engineer, with his brother William as his assistant. On 26th June the Douglass workforce returned to the Bishop Rock to continue with the project, only to find the survivors of the BELINDA huddled together inside the partly completed tower. This limestone carrying Cardiff cutter, had run into the Bishop Rock during thick fog. Her Captain managed to get his vessel off the Rock, although he failed to realise the extent of the damage. Within minutes the BELINDA sank, but all her crew reached the safety of the lighthouse. After the Douglass workforce found them, they were put on board the Trinity tender and taken to St. Mary's Island. [8]

The Bishop Rock lighthouse progressed with its tower of solid granite

BISHOP ROCK LIGHTHOUSE.

The first Bishop Rock lighthouse built of granite - 1858
with feint outline of new tower in background.
Reproduced with kind permission of Trinity House

blocks dovetailed together and with thick copper bolts added for extra security. This process continued until the base was 45ft (13.7m) AHWST. Above this mass of stonework, the granite walls were erected. At the base they were 4ft 9ins (1.45m) thick, which tapered externally to 2ft (610mm) thick at the course of masonry at the tower's cornice. Moulded granite stone was then positioned on top, with the lantern gallery surrounded by iron railings. On to the railings was fixed a steel flagstaff. A formidable copper lantern which had been constructed by W. Wilkins & Co. Ltd., London, was then erected on top of the tower. It was 14ft (4.27m) in diameter and 28ft (8.53m) high to the top of its domed roof. [1]

Bishop Rock - First Lit

After 7 years of; at times, life threatening work, the Bishop Rock light was first lit on the 1st September 1858. Its oil burning light was positioned at 110ft (33.5m) AHWST and was recorded as being visible between 14-16 nautical miles. Its optical apparatus consisted of dioptric lenses with 8 reflectors and 19 prisms (13 above and 6 below the refractors). The optical assembly was supplied and commissioned by Le Paute of Paris. The lamp was a fountain type unit with four circular wicks and was supplied by W. Wilkins & Co. Ltd., of London. [1]

Following the successful completion, Prince Albert; Consort to Queen Victoria, remarked during a speech given at a meeting at the Headquarters of Trinity House in Tower Hill, London, that the effort was "a triumph of engineering skill and perseverance". [1] On the inside of the lighthouse there is a bronze plaque that commemorates the construction work and reads: *'This tower was erected by the Corporation of Trinity House of Deptford Strond, in London. The first stone was laid on the 14th July 1852, in the sixteenth year of the reign of Her Majesty Queen Victoria.*

His Grace the Duke of Wellington, Master;
Captain John Henry Pelly, Bart., Deputy Master.

The lowest stone was afterwards laid in the chasm of the rock, at one foot below low water spring tides, on the 30th July, 1852.
The stonework of the tower was finished on the 28th August, 1857,
His Royal Highness the Prince Consort, Master;
Captain John Shepard Deputy Master.

The successful termination of this most difficult undertaking was accomplished without the loss of life or serious accident to any person employed.

DEO SOLO GLORIA

James Walker Engineer   *N. Douglass Superintendent'*

When the final accounts were produced on the completion of the lighthouse, the total was £36,559. [1]

Should be No Light Levy

Trinity House Elder Brethren still maintained that the Bishop Rock lighthouse should be devoid of any levy for its upkeep. They told the Board of Trade; which now decided on the levies to be collected, that when considering the Bishop Rock lighthouse had been started prior to the introduction of the Merchant Shipping Act of 1854 (when a major part of the Corporations responsibilities were taken over by the Board of Trade), shipowners had not requested the building of this lighthouse or offered in the normal way to pay for its upkeep. They also pointed out that the levies received from the St. Agnes lighthouse would more than cover the upkeep of both lights. The Board of Trade ignored the request of Trinity House and imposed a heavy toll on the Bishop Rock light, but records show that this was not enforced until 1859. [1] Four keepers were necessary for a rock based lighthouse such as the Bishop Rock, three were on duty at any one time and the other on shore leave. Each month, the man on leave would return and another would take his turn for well-earned leave with his family.

Scurvy Amongst the Keepers

On the 8th July 1859, the Royal Commission of Buoys, Beacons and Lights carried out a survey of the Bishop Rock lighthouse. They arrived on board the steamer VIVID during an exceptional dry spell. The conditions of the keepers was reported as poor with serious problems due to scurvy. The inspectors strongly recommended that more fruit and fresh vegetables should be provided. When the next relief boat arrived, gallons of lime juice were among the supplies. On completion of their visit, the inspectors requested that the fog bell be rung. In their report they recorded that, even though they were only a quarter of a mile away, on a clear day with the steamer quiet, they could not hear the bell [5]. This was to prove a salutary warning.

One of the Most Exposed Lighthouses

During the winter months of 1860, a device was fitted to the base of the Bishop Rock lighthouse, to measure the force of the Atlantic waves. The apparatus was similar in design to one constructed by Thomas Stevenson and consisted of a unit resembling a railway buffer with a sleeper fixed across two oil-filled plungers. A hydraulic hose was fitted between these two points with the other end connected to a gauge. The device was securely positioned and each day readings were recorded. The principle of the gauge was simple; only the highest reading would show with the needle held by a ratchet-operated cog. George Findlay wrote: *"During a fierce storm the gauge broke at a reading of 7010 pounds per square foot. The highest recorded reading that Mr. Stevenson had previously taken was 6083 pounds per square foot, on the 29th March 1845 at the Bell Rock lighthouse in Scotland"*. [6] This proved that the Bishop Rock tower, was one of the most exposed lighthouses in the World.

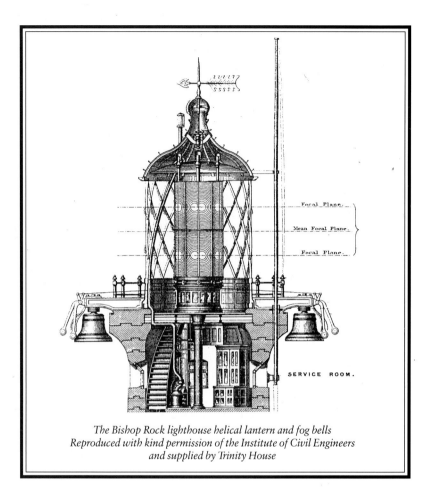

The Bishop Rock lighthouse helical lantern and fog bells
Reproduced with kind permission of the Institute of Civil Engineers
and supplied by Trinity House

The destructive power of the Atlantic provided visual proof on the 30th January 1860, when it tore away the massive brass access ladder and ripped off the heavy iron stormproof entrance door. Plate glass windows 12.5mm thick were smashed near the top of the tower, with the force of the waves overshooting the lighthouse. During this tremendous storm, the power of the sea wrenched the 3cwt (151kg) brass fog bell from its gun-metal mounting and cast it onto the rocks below. A successive wave picked up the bell like a discarded paper cup and tossed it into the sea. Although the keepers sent up distress flares, it was not until the morning of the 1st February that a boat was able to reach them. Even then a landing was impossible, but a leather bag containing a letter to Captain Hugh Tregarthen; the surveyor for lighthouses and James Douglass's father-in-law, was pulled through the sea to the relief boat. Captain Tregarthen later estimated the damage at over £1000, which was a considerable cost when compared to the original construction accounts for the Bishop Rock lighthouse of £36,000. A new 5cwt (254kg) brass bell was installed during these repairs. [1]

About to Die

Relentless storms continued with even more ferocity and on the night of the 20th April 1874, the keepers of the Bishop Rock light believed they were about to die. Waves in excess of 120ft (36.6m) high cleared the top of the tower and smashed the reinforced plate glass in the lantern. Seawater cascaded down through the interior of the tower with such force, that the keepers had to tie themselves to the stairway for safety. The noise was deafening, with each successive wave causing the structure to shake. But James Walker's design held firm, which must stand as a tribute to all those men who built the lighthouse. During the summer season James Douglass took his workforce back to the Bishop Rock and strengthened the tower with massive wide iron bands, bolted through every course of the lower external walls.

Fog and the SCHILLER

Fog must be one of the worst problems for the mariner to encounter. With radar systems and satellite navigation of modern times, this matter can be virtually overcome. But fog and a catalogue of events led to the sinking of the passenger liner SCHILLER, on the 7th May 1875, with the loss of 313 lives. [8]

The SCHILLER left New York on the 27th April 1875, on her voyage to Hamburg. Her first port of arrival would be a short stop off at Plymouth. This grand liner had a gross tonnage of 3421 tons and was built by Napiers of Glasgow. She was launched from the shipyard in August 1873.

On the 7th May 1875, the SCHILLER was proceeding at about 4 knots towards the Isles of Scilly, attempting to find her way through a dense blanket of fog. Her Commanding Officer, Captain Thomas, asked the passengers for volunteers, to look out for the Bishop Rock lighthouse. The first person who spotted the light would be awarded with a bottle of champagne. Other passengers strained their ears for the sound of the expected fog bell, but nothing was heard.

Captain Thomas believed the SCHILLER was too far to the east and changed course on a more westerly heading. AT 22:00 the SCHILLER hit the Retarriers Rocks. Distress flares were launched, but it is reported that the keepers on the Bishop Rock lighthouse, mistook them for the customary flares sent up on the arrival of a ship into port. Even the St. Mary's coastguards were of the same opinion and took no action. [8]

As the SCHILLER's passengers began to panic, Captain Thomas was forced to fire his revolver over the heads of the hysterical people in order to gain control. Suddenly the SCHILLER was hit by a gigantic wave that toppled the ship's funnel which smashed two of the lifeboats as it came crashing down. Two other lifeboats became stuck in their davits, another capsized at it was being lowered into the sea, which in turn threw its occupants to their death. As one other loaded lifeboat was being lowered, a hugh wave smashed it to pieces against the side of the liner. From the original eight lifeboats on board, only two were successfully loaded with passengers and set adrift in the fog.

Near the SCHILLER's midship saloon, were gathered 50 women and children, when without warning a succession of gigantic waves washed them overboard. As dawn broke and the fog began to lift, a Cornish fishing boat from Sennen Cove arrived at the unbelievable tragic scene and sent up its distress flares. Within an hour a flotilla of small boats, coastguards, fishing boats and the steamer LADY OF THE ISLES, joined in the desperate search for survivors. Two men were found exhausted and suffering from exposure, clinging to a rock beside the stricken SCHILLER. Twelve hours later the loaded lifeboats drifted into Tresco with a total of 26 men and one woman on board. From the original complement of passengers and crew, only 42 survived out of a total of 355 people. [8]

Keepers Letter to his Wife

The sinking of the SCHILLER had a devastating effect on James Daniel the Assistant Head Keeper of the Bishop Rock, who wrote to his wife following the tragic disaster. The following transcript is reproduced with the kind permission of Trinity House, with an acknowledgement shown towards the Association of Lighthouse Keepers. The letter reads:

"Bishop Rock, May 10th,
Dear Wife,

With heart sick grief I write to inform you of the dreadful wreck that has happened here, less than half a mile inside of us, on Friday inst. I had been on watch up to eight p.m., when I was relieved by the man on duty whilst our principal keeper was on shore, but seeing the fog setting in I still kept at the lantern and ordered the bell to be set going at 8.40 p.m. - fog very thick. I timed the bell properly at six strokes per minute, and saw that all was right. I left the lantern at 10 p.m. and went to my bunk, but could not sleep.

At 11.35 p.m., William Mortimer (fellow keeper) came running down and called to me and said he could see a vessel on the rocks. I jumped up and went out to the parapet without stopping to dress, and saw the masthead and starboard light of a large steamer. She was burning blue lights and firing off guns and rockets. She seemed to be sinking. The last gun was fired at 1.30 a.m. on the 8th inst. I relieved G. Gould at 4 a.m.

Fog again raised at 6 a.m., and I could then just see the top mast of the

*Classic drawing showing interior, exteric
Reproduced with k*

base of Walker's Bishop Rock lighthouse
on of Trinity House

vessel out of the water. We could count about twenty-six people in the rigging. I could see one lady in the lee side of the rigging with two males beside her. She was in a sitting position, I should think lashed. It was a dreadful sight. At about 7 a.m. the mast fell and I suppose everyone perished, but I still hope a few or some might have been saved.

On Sunday three bodies floated past us, and this afternoon more have passed close to us. No one knows what was felt in this house by all hands to see so many of our dear fellow creatures suffering and dying so near to us. Their sufferings must have been severe, for it was a cold drizzling rain all night, wind w.s.w. I think you had better take this letter, together with my compliments, to John Branfield, Lloyd's agent.

I remain your affectionate husband,
James Daniel."

Structurally Unsafe

A further 7 years would elapse before positive steps were taken to build a new lighthouse on the Bishop Rock. This was finally put into operation following a tremendous storm during the winter months of 1881. When the damage to the lighthouse was surveyed after this storm, pieces of granite weighing about 56lbs (25kg) had been wrenched from the external face of the tower. With these sections only just above the high water mark, James Douglass informed the Elder Brethren of Trinity House that the damage was seriously affecting the structural safety of the tower. [1]

William Tregarthen Douglass and the Third Lighthouse

The contract for the new lighthouse began in the Spring of 1883 under the supervision of William Tregarthen Douglass (son of Sir James Douglass and Mary Tregarthen Douglass) as resident engineer for the project. Commencement had been delayed for 12 months until the Eddystone light was completed on the 18th May 1882. At this time the twin screw steamer HERCULES was brought into service for the project. This 130 ton registered steamer *(of 45 nautical horse power)* had been specially built in 1870 for the Little Basses lighthouse contract in Sri Lanka (Ceylon). All the plant and equipment used during the building of the Eddystone was taken on board the HERCULES to St. Mary's Island where a large plot of land had been leased by Trinity House close to the pier [3].

All of the granite which would form the casing and upper portion of the new Bishop Rock lighthouse, was obtained from the Eddystone quarries at Delank in Cornwall. These blocks were then carefully dressed to specified templates and erected in temporary sections at the quarry. When they were required on site they would be loaded on to the HERCULES and taken to the Rock. The dressing work to the granite blocks entailed cutting dovetails horizontally as well as vertically. This intricate work would be needed from the foundation course of masonry to the level above the original service room, or course 62.

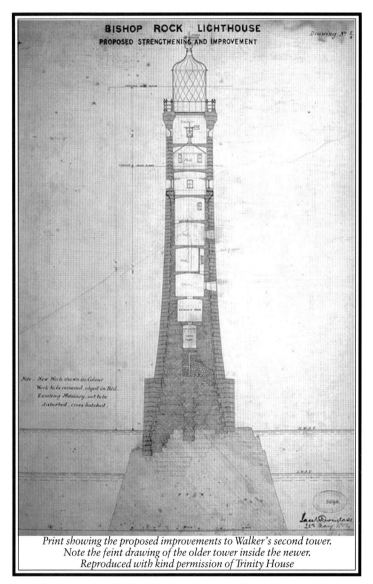

Print showing the proposed improvements to Walker's second tower.
Note the feint drawing of the older tower inside the newer.
Reproduced with kind permission of Trinity House

All of these granite blocks weighed between 2 to 3 tons and great care was taken during the transportation to the Rock. When the casing blocks were positioned, they each had a male dovetail 6ins (150mm) deep at its inner end to ensure a firm and true adhesion to the existing tower face.

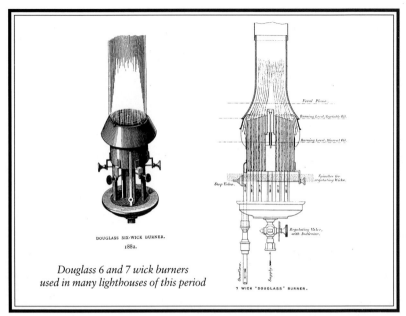

DOUGLASS SIX-WICK BURNER.
1882.

*Douglass 6 and 7 wick burners
used in many lighthouses of this period*

7 WICK "DOUGLASS" BURNER.

Apart from this, the blocks were also dovetailed to each other, with a joint tolerance of plus or minus 3mm.

More Substantial Base

James Douglass's design required that the cylindrical base of the tower be raised to a significant level above high water. This would provide two important factors. Not only a substantial base, but also an efficient landing stage for supplies. The cylindrical base of the present tower is 41ft (12.5m) in diameter and 40ft (12.2m) above the foundation rock. Access is provided from the Rock to the landing stage, by gun metal hoops *(dog steps)* set into the granite. Central to this landing stage would be the 32ft (9.75m) diameter base of the tower.

With a workforce of 30 men work began on the tedious and often dangerous task of dressing the granite of the existing tower and foundation rock. This operation was as follows: *'Holes were drilled by manual labour in the face of the tower, then the granite was plugged by means of steel plugs and feathers, and the dovetails were dressed to a template by double and single cast-steel points. One mason and one hammer man worked together preparing for each block of new masonry and on average completed their work in rather under two days for a dovetail stone, the dressing for a stone having no dovetail at its inner end, occupying the remainder of the second day'* [1]

24

Because of the dangerous Atlantic rollers that swept across the Rock, lifelines were secured to a chain that encircled the tower. Each man had his own lifeline and on numerous occasions the sea completely engulfed the workforce, but none of them were washed away.

To use every available chance of continuing the difficult task of dressing the granite, William Douglass lodged 12 of his men in the lighthouse. When the weather or sea conditions permitted progress, these men were already on the Rock. There was no record how these men were accommodated or where they slept.

A specially designed crane was anchored to the gallery of the existing tower, that was capable of covering the full circumference of the lighthouse. To prevent any damage to the granite blocks the hoisting cables were fitted with a padded iron cage capable of holding 2-4 tons. Even though the crane was hand-powered, it served the project extremely well and without any major problems.

HERCULES and Granite Blocks

Off-loading the granite blocks from the HERCULES was a delicate operation with the steamer's winch and crane lifting them on to the landing stage. On numerous occasions these blocks would be hit by the heavy sea causing them to swing uncontrollably. This problem was overcome by reversing the winch and quickly lowering the granite block into the sea. When the stone was comparatively still the crane lifted it on to the landing stage, but even at this point there were problems from the swell. Thick coconut fibre (*coir*) mats were placed strategically against the tower to stop the blocks from being damaged. At times it was recorded in William Douglass's report *"that a sudden rise or fall of the vessel on a wave, would frequently cause the block to rise or fall 6ft (1.8m)"*. Only one block was lost overboard due to an abnormal swell which caused it to be thrown from the HERCULES into the sea. Luckily the incident occurred near the end of the working season and did not cause any delay to the project [1].

First Block Laid

The first stone for the foundations was set into position on the north-west side of the existing Bishop Rock tower on the 25th May 1883. By the beginning of the winter season 57 stones up to the 9th course were finished and some of those in the course above. By the 11th May 1886, all the granite blocks up to the 62nd course were completed and the demolition work for the remaining old tower had started.

Demolition of Old Tower

The first job of the demolition programme was the removal of the lantern and lighting apparatus. This was lowered to the landing stage then put onto the HERCULES to be taken to another lighthouse. On top of the completed 62nd course a timber staging was erected that extended clear of the line of the foundation rocks below. A small railway and truck was fixed to this staging. As each of the dismantled stones was lowered by the crane it was deposited into the truck, then pushed to the end of the staging and tipped into the sea.

Once the existing floors of the lighthouse were removed, another crane was erected and positioned in the centre of the tower. This crane consisted of a hollow wrought iron mast with a 40ft (12.9m) top section surmounted by a Trinity House floating lantern and a double flashing catoptric light. This temporary light consisted of an 8ft (2.44m) cylindrical lantern with 2 groups of 21 inch (533mm) parabolic silvered reflectors (3 in a group). The light source came in the form of a 2 wick Douglass burner to each reflector; the fuel used was paraffin. Each flash of light from these reflectors was equal to 16,000 candle power. Although temporary, this light exceeded the original lighting apparatus by 1000 candle power. Two iron jibs were bolted to the crane's mast that were moveable to allow coverage of the full circumference of the lighthouse. To operate the crane, a steam boiler and winch were bolted to the vertical base platform and enclosed with a masonry breakwater [1].

New Works

The building of the new section of the tower began on the 26th June 1886. This consisted of a further 28 courses of masonry, to increase the height of the tower from the old lighthouse by 40ft (12.32m) and to give four extra rooms. Compared to the arduous task of dressing the original granite tower and the setting of the foundations to the 62nd course, these final courses averaged between one and two each day. By the 30th August all the masonry and remaining stonework was completed. The overall height of the tower from foundations to the top of the lantern is 160ft 9ins (49m) with the focal plane of the light set at 144ft 4ins (44m) AHWST The average thickness of granite stones used in the construction of the circular casing was 3ft 6ins (1.07m). The additional granite used to construct the new Bishop Rock lighthouse amounted to 3220 tons, with a completion time of less than three and a half years.

Chance Brothers and Douglass Helical Lantern

On completion of the gallery, a Douglass-designed lantern was erected. This lantern was constructed and installed by Chance Brothers of Birmingham, from the specifications given by its Chief Engineer, F.A. Richey. It was 14ft (4.3m) in diameter and 31ft (9.5m) to the top of its weather vane. Its 15ft (4.6m) high glazed section was positioned on top of a cast iron pedestal base. On top of the gun metal- framed lantern were steel rafters covered in thick sheets of copper that formed its roof. This was surmounted by a drum ventilator and weather vane. The light source was supplied by two eight-wicked Douglass oil lamps. Paraffin for these lamps was pumped from the service room below.

F.A. Richey (Uncle Bill)
Reproduced with kind permission of Bill Dimmock

Chief Engineer Richey - Hyper-radial Optics

The Chance Brothers optics, also designed by F.A. Richey, consisted of 2 layered tiers of lenses. Each tier contained ten lenses set at a horizontal angle of 36^0 and a vertical angle of 80^0. Each lens consisted of a central bull's eye optic with 17 ring prisms above and below. The two oil burners were positioned behind the optics, one above the other. In clear weather the lower burner would be operational and produced a 40,000 candle power beam through the optic. If the keepers could not see the St. Agnes light five miles away, they would use both burners which produced a beam of 230,000 candle power. The framework of the optical apparatus was specially constructed from a heavy steel section designed to resist the sudden shock of waves hitting the tower. The duration of the light sequence was a 4.75 second flash followed by a 4.25 second eclipse, then another flash of 4.75 seconds ended by an eclipse of 46.25 seconds.

Compressed Air instead of Clockwork

The service room below the lantern contained two 100 gallon pressurised oil tanks which supplied the 250 degrees flashpoint paraffin to the burners. There were also two 1.5 h.p. *'Davey'* steam engines *(with a coke consumption of 14 tons per annum)* used to drive the air compressors. In turn, the compressed air was used to revolve the heavy optical apparatus because the normal clockwork system was not powerful enough. The compressed air also powered the gallery winch which was used to land the lighthouse stores. It was normal procedure for the keepers to operate the *'Davey'* engines during the daytime to ensure a full charge of air for the night.

Fog Gun

An explosive fog-gun was installed after it was finally agreed by the Corporation, that the existing 5cwt (254kg) brass fog-bell was useless. During the five years that William Tregarthen Douglass had been supervising the Bishop Rock project, six ships had been wrecked within a five mile radius. Masters of these vessels even stated in the Board of Trade Inquiry reports, that none of them had heard the feeble bell. Trinity House must have known that the present fog system was inadequate, for there had been many complaints and warnings. The tragic loss of the SCHILLER was a prime example. The failure of the Corporation to implement a more suitable warning system within the 12 year period leading up to the completion of the new lighthouse, can only be labelled as bordering on the irresponsible. After the introduction of the gun there were no further wreckings until 1892 where the cause was attributed to fog. [7]

This new fog-gun consisted of a hollow steel barrel fixed to the lantern. It had a safety feature which only allowed the mechanism to be fired when it was in its correct position. For loading purposes the barrel was lowered, then primed with 4oz (113gms) of guncotton and a fulminate of mercury detonator. When sited in its correct position, it was wired to a hand operated dynamo-electric firing unit kept inside the lantern. During foggy or heavy mist conditions this gun was fired every 5 minutes.

First Lit - Cost of Project

The Bishop Rock lighthouse first showed its light on the 25th October 1887. The cost of its construction was £64,889. When comparing the finances spent on erecting lighthouses on the Bishop Rock, James Walker's fated cast iron pile tower was £12,500, with his granite successor almost £34,560. In total the Corporation of Trinity House spent £111,949. [7]

The FALKLAND

Even with the new lighthouse and adequate fog warning facilities, the weather and the treacherous Atlantic Ocean still took its toll on shipping.

Although the advent of steam and much straighter courses being run brought about a marked reduction in shipping incidents, those under sail were still being affected.

On the 22nd June 1901, the four masted barque FALKLAND was enroute from Tacoma, Washington, USA, with a cargo of wheat bound for Falmouth. This 2676 ton vessel had a complement of 28 crew, her Master, Captain Gracie and his wife and small daughter. With the wind increasing to gale force and the sea becoming very choppy, the FALKLAND hit the Bishop Rock with such force that she carved a deep gouge in its surface.

Captain Gracie had seen the lighthouse from two miles away, but the wind had blown the FALKLAND directly in line with Bishop Rock. As he tried to force the ship away from the Rock the mainyard struck the lighthouse. With her side breached, the holds quickly filled with water. As the keepers tried to get lines on board the FALKLAND, the heavy seas dragged her clear. The Captain's wife and daughter and 23 crew, managed to get clear of the strickened ship in two of the vessel's lifeboats. Captain Gracie, the Mate, steward and two crewmen, went down with the FALKLAND.

Two hours after the tragic incident, the St. Agnes lifeboat found the crowded lifeboats from the FALKLAND and towed them into St. Mary's. Nearly two days after the wrecking, the body of one of the missing crewmen was washed ashore in Hell Bay, lashed to a chicken coop.

A keeper using an old M/F radio,
similar to the type used throughout the service

Incandescent Mantle Burners and Radio

In 1913 the Bishop Rock lighthouse was fitted with a radio telephone, which allowed the keepers to have direct contact with other rescue services and the Trinity House shore base in Penzance.

During the summer of 1922, David Hood, the Engineer-in-Chief for the Corporation, upgraded the light source at Bishop Rock with the introduction of a new incandescent mantle burner. This particular system was devised by him and based upon the invention of Arthur Kitson in 1901. Pressurised paraffin was fed into a retort below the mantle then heated. This produced an inflammable gas which was then lit above the mantle. This system effectively trebled the light source, of previous multi-wicked lamps.

Clear Weather and the WESTERN FRONT

Not all of the ships wrecked near the Bishop Rock were due to the weather, the sea or the reef.

With a nett tonnage of 5685 tons, the WESTERN FRONT was an American steamer registered in Seattle and built in 1917 by the Skinner and Eddy Corporation. On the 2nd July 1921 she began her voyage from Jacksonville, USA, with a 7000 ton cargo which consisted of highly inflammable materials such as turpentine, naptha and resin.

When the WESTERN FRONT was about twenty miles from the Bishop Rock lighthouse, on the 11th July, her Captain was told that a fire had broken out in one of the holds. All efforts to extinguish the fire failed. The Captain radioed his position and his 'Mayday' alarm to the coastguards and the St. Mary's lifeboat ELSIE was despatched to the scene. On arrival, the ELSIE took on board 40 of the WESTERN FRONT'S crew. The steamer BRITISH EARL also answered the distress call and with the careful seamanship of her Captain, she was able to pull alongside and rescue the remaining crew, her Captain and an injured able-seaman.

By the time everyone on board the WESTERN FRONT had been taken off, she had drifted to within seven miles of the Bishop Rock lighthouse and was ablaze from bow to stern. On seeing this the lighthouse keepers radioed their concern, as it appeared the blazing ship was on a collision course with the Rock. As it drifted within 2 miles of the lighthouse, the WESTERN FRONT exploded in a hugh ball of flames. The shock of the explosion shook the tower. [8]

1973 - Electricity and Helipad

In 1973 the vaporised paraffin incandescent mantle lamps were removed and the lighthouse converted to electricity. Three years later difficulties in supplying stores and provisions to the lighthouse were overcome when Trinity House built a helicopter pad above the lantern. For 16 years various changes

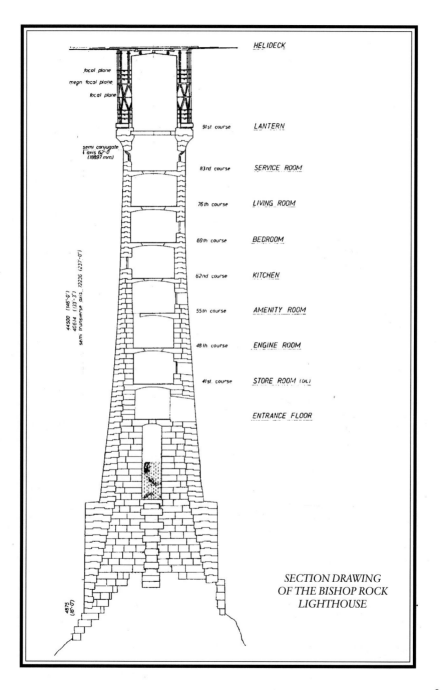

HELIDECK

focal plane
mean focal plane
focal plane

91st course   LANTERN

semi conjugate
axis 62'0
(18897 mm)

83rd course   SERVICE ROOM

76th course   LIVING ROOM

69th course   BEDROOM

62nd course   KITCHEN

55th course   AMENITY ROOM

48th course   ENGINE ROOM

41st course   STORE ROOM (OIL)

ENTRANCE FLOOR

44500 (146'-0")
40614 (133'-3")
semi transverse axis 72236 (237'-0")

4875
(16'-0")

SECTION DRAWING
OF THE BISHOP ROCK
LIGHTHOUSE

31

were made to the lighthouse until, in December 1992, the conversion to automatic operation was completed. [9]

Today the Bishop Rock lighthouse continues its lonely vigil providing 2 white flashes every 15 seconds. Its light is visible for 24 nautical miles at an intensity of 2.8 million candle power. Its automatic atmospheric sensor, which activates when visibility is less than 2 miles, switches on the fog signal that gives 2 blasts every 90 seconds. The operation of the Bishop Rock light is monitored by the Trinity House Operations Control Centre at Harwich. [9]

The Bishop Rock lighthouse has long been associated with the winning of the famous BLUE RIBAND award for the fastest crossing of the Atlantic by a passenger carrying vessel. The timing of the crossing was taken from the Ambrose lightvessel; now a light-tower, off the eastern seaboard of the USA until it passed the Bishop Rock. One of the most famous liners to win this award was the United States Line vessel UNITED STATES which, on her maiden voyage, averaged a speed of nearly 40 knots. The most recent award winner was the entrepreneur Richard Branson who, with his fast boat VIRGIN ATLANTIC 2 won the award in 1986.

Photograph of Handel Bluer
by kind permission of Andrew Beseley

To relieve the boredom of living on an isolated rock station the keepers devised various ideas to continue their sporting activity. Principal Keeper Handel (Andy) Bluer utilised the helipad at Bishop Rock for a golf course. By means of drilling a hole in a ball and attaching it to a long length of cord, he was able to practice his swing at 147 ft (44.8m) above sea level. When on shore Handel Bluer is actively involved with the Cornish Silver Bands and is a regular figure at the Trinity House National Lighthouse Centre in Penzance. Another keeper; Tony Elvers, was recorded on television tap-dancing in top hat and tails to raise money for the 1986 B.B.C. *'Children in Need'* appeal. During the late 1960's a television documentary titled *'The Last Lighthouse'* was made and graphically showed the cramped and, even at that time, somewhat primitive conditions endured by the keepers serving on offshore stations.

On the 15th December 1992, Bishop Rock lighthouse was finally automated with the keepers leaving the station for the last time. However the last keeper Peter Robson refused to be involved with the press coverage of this event. For reasons better known to himself, he ignored the newspaper reporter and went home. It was then found necessary to find another keeper who would be prepared to stand in for the *'last keeper.'* One of the keepers who was ashore, Colin Jones A.K., was traced to a local *'hostelry'* and unceremoniously dragged out for the publicity stunt. He was dressed up in his survival suit and taken to the Bishop Rock for the final photos.

Many years have passed since the Bishop Rock lighthouse was first established. No-one can doubt its importance as a warning signal for shipping. Even with modern electronic navigational aids, the vision of this tower of light is welcomed by all who pass this majestic tower.

* * * * * * * * * * * *

Reference Sources

1. Douglass, J.N., 'The Bishop Rock lighthouses', Minutes of the Proceedings of the Institute of Civil Engineers, Vol. 108, 207-244 (1892)
2. Trinity House Minutes (January 1851). Guildhall Library
3. Williams, T., 'Life of Sir James Nicholas Douglass' (1900)
4. Trinity House Records (1965. Guildhall Library
5. Report of the Royal Commission on Buoys, Buoyage and Lights, 2793-XXV (1861)
6. Findlay, A.G., 'Pharology', 26th edn., Richard Holmes Laurie, Fleet St., London, UK (1885)
7. Williams, T., 'Life of William Douglass' (1923)
8. Isles of Scilly Coastguard Records (1960)
9. Trinity House Records (1994) Tower Hill, London
10. Trinity House Minute Books (1680). Guildhall Library

Special Thanks

During many hours of research at the Trinity House Engineering Directorate, certain members of staff have willingly assisted with finding special drawings and other snippets of information for use in the various publications. Most of these times, disturbed their lunch breaks, so my special thanks to John Sim, Frank Celaco and Alan Spooner. The wealth of information provided is remarkable and always given with a true sense of humour to a very probing researcher. I must point out that the wonderful photograph of the Bishop Rock lighthouse used on the front cover was freely given by Frank Gibson. Also Andrew Beseley has provided several photos which will be used in future publications.

'NEW AGE DRAWING'
Showing how Trinity House
Engineering Department
are using the most modern techniques of
3D computerised drawing facilities

35

ACKNOWLEDGEMENTS FROM THE AUTHOR

A special *'thank you'* is given to all those people and organisations who have so *'willingly'* assisted in ensuring the details portrayed in this publication were *'factual'*. These include Ian Beevis; Tony Elvers; Kenneth Sutton-Jones; Dr. Ken Trethewey; Gerry Douglass-Sherwood and the A.L.K.; Jane Wilson for Trinity House; AB Pharos Marine Ltd., Brentwood; the archivists for the Truro and Plymouth Record Offices; the Institute of Civil Engineers in London and the unsung heroes of the Engineering Department of Trinity House and their Director. Mention must also be made of the anonymous Trinity House photographers and draught *'persons'* who have provided a pictorial record that allows a wonderful insight into this lighthouse story and to Richard Laughton for his technical support. The photographic skill of Frank Gibson, St. Mary's Island, Isles of Scilly; Andrew Beseley of Reawla, Cornwall are most gratefully acknowledged. Help has also been provided by the Coastguards of the Isles of Scilly and the R.N.L.I. at Poole, Dorset. The Isles of Scilly Museum has supplied an abundance of information, including a small item that was originally published in 1950, titled *'Shipwrecks Around The Isles Of Scilly'* by Charlotte Dorrien Smith. A wonderful insight to local shipping incidents is shown in this publication.
The assistance provided by various lighthouse keepers, such as Handel Bluer B.E.M., give a marvellous view of life on a desolate rock-based station.
Like all jigsaw puzzles, it cannot be considered finished until every piece is in place. This story has been just like that.

THANK YOU ALL

Martin Boyle

Association of Lighthouse Keepers
The Secretary,
Association of Lighthouse Keepers,
2, Queen's Cottages,
Queen's Road,
Lydd,
Kent TN29 9ND

Trinity House National Lighthouse Museum
Wharf Road,
Penzance,
Cornwall TR18 4BN
Tel: 01736 360077

Scotland's Lighthouse Museum
Kinnaird Head,
Fraserburgh, AB43 5DU
Tel: 01346 511022
Fax: 01346 511033

Leading Lights Magazine
Peter Williams Associates,
c/o Haven Lightship,
Milford Marina,
Milford Haven,
SA73 3AF
Tel: (+44) 01646 698055/698825

Bishops Printers
Banana House,
Goldsmith Avenue,
Portsmouth, Hants, PO4 0BT
Tel: (01705) 825883

Very Helpful and friendly
family style printing company.
Provides an exceptional, quality service
Highly recommended

Lighthouse
Digest
P.O. Box 1690
Wells, Maine 04090
USA
Tel: 00 1 207-646--515

U.S. Lighthouse Society,
Wayne Wheeler,
244 Kearney Street,
5th Floor,
SAN FRANCISCO
CA 94108
USA

International Association of Lighthouse Authorities (IALA)
c/o Paul Ridgeway
3, The Green,
Ketton,
Stamford.
Lincolnshire.
PE9 3RA
Tel: 01780 721628
Fax: 01780 721980

Klaus Kern produces this wonderful magazine with a theme that deals mainly with stamps and postcards. However this regularly produced magazine is in German but contains many wonderful lighthouse stories. A must for the Lighthouse Enthusiast.

LEUCHTFEUR
(Lighthouse Enthusiasts Magazine)
Klaus Kern,
Pestalozzistrasse 28,
D-65428 Rüsselsheim,
Allemagne/Germany
Tel: Germany 06142-81607

Sweden's Lighthouse Society
Esbjörn Hillberg,
HUS 154,
S-43082 Donsö,
Sweden
Tel: (+46) (0) 31-972148
Fax: (+46) (0) 31-970623

An exceptional range of nautical and other maritime books are listed in this bookseller's catalogue. These lists are regularly updated and if there is any book published, the very helpful staff will ensure every effort is made to obtain the one required. Very cost-effective.

Mainmast Books
251 Copnor Road,
Portsmouth,
Hants, PO3 5EE
Tel: (01705) 645555
Fax: (01705) 695723

Frank E. Gibson
Photographer,
St. Mary's Island,
Isle of Scilly,
TR21 0JQ,
Cornwall.
Tel: (01720) 422645

*Photographer of numerous Cornish Lights
and a very modest man with regards to his
exceptional talents.*

*This professional photographer
has even hung from the side of
a helicopter in rather bad weather
to obtain the right shot.
His library is well worth a visit.*

Andrew Besley
Photographer &
Photographic Library,
2 Reawla Lane,
Reawla,
Nr. Hayle,
Tr27 5HQ,
Cornwall.
Tel: (01736) 850086

"SCILLY"
(Up to date)
A. H. Read & Son,
Porthmellon Works,
St. Mary's,
Isles of Scilly,
TR21 0JY
Tel: (01720) 422718

*A wonderful magazine and newsletter
produced monthly for the Isles of Scilly.
It gives a marvellous insight to the Isles,
numerous stories and information on the
best places to visit or stay.
Very interesting reading.*

*This company welcomes enquiries from the
Lighthouse enthusiast. They are more than
willing to pass any comments or
communications to Kenneth Sutton-Jones*

AB Pharos Marine Ltd.
77 High Street,
Brentford,
Middlesex,
TW8 0AP
Tel: (0181) 568879

ALADDIN'S CAVE CHANDELRY
Deacon's Boatyard,
Bridge Road,
Burseldon,
Southampton,
Hants,
SO3 8AW
Tel: (01703) 402182
Fax: (01703) 406381

*Apart from the normal requirements suplied
by any Chandler, this business is very
enthusiastic about lighthouse publications
and hold an extensive collection.*

To obtain a free list of 'LIGHTHOUSES OF ENGLAND AND WALES' booklets and the details of our 'NO OBLIGATION TO BUY', bookclub, send a S.A.E. to B & T PUBLICATIONS, 10, Orchard Way, Highfield, Southampton, SO17 1RD, U.K.

To accompany this collection of 'LIGHTHOUSES OF ENGLAND AND WALES', the author has compiled two special publications. The first booklet is titled: 'LIGHTHOUSES: FOUR COUNTRIES, ONE AIM' and gives an easy to read insight into the Corporation of Trinity House, the Commissioners of Irish Lights, the Commissioners of Northern Lights, Private Lighthouse owners, Royal Letter-Patents and the services which are provided today. This booklet also gives an account of the designers and builders of the lighthouses around the coasts of the British Isles.

The second publication provided a detailed account of the various light sources, fuels, reflectors and optical apparatus, lanterns and fog warning systems and an insight to those designers and manufacturers who supplied these items. Titled: 'LIGHTHOUSES: TO LIGHT THEIR WAY', this booklet had been produced with many archive photos and pictorials which have been provided by the various Lighthouse Authorities and by the author of 'PHAROS: YESTERDAY, TODAY AND TOMORROW', Kenneth Sutton-Jones. This author has also assisted in a major way, by ensuring that the relative technical details are correct. This help has been greatly appreciated by this author. Each of these booklets can be obtained from bookshops or direct from the publisher, (POST FREE IN UK).

Also available from B & T PUBLICATIONS: Database of the Lighthouses of Great Britain and Ireland. Full colour Windows® (3.1, 3.11 and 95) software. References and locations for over 350 lighthouses. Details of characteristic, fog signals, lat/long, type of tower, date established, history and sources of information. Enlarged and updated each year. Modify the database to suit your own needs. Comprehensive Search and Help functions. Suitable for PCs 386 and above with 4Mb RAM and VGA screen. Requires 2MB hard disk space and 3.5" floppy drive. Not suitable for Apple-Mac.

Why not join the PHAROS PEN PALS CLUB?
Details from the Secretary:
Ian Beevis, 13 Chyngton Way, Seaford, East Sussex BN25 4JB U.K.